BUILD YOUR OWN ADVENTURE

CONTENTS

MEET THE PRINCESSES

Mulan

Growing up in ancient China, Mulan is torn between bringing honour to her family and satisfying her thirst for adventure. By becoming a skilled warrior, she fulfils both of her dreams.

READY FOR AN ADVENTURE!

KHAN

Khan is Mulan's horse and her loyal companion. They love to go on adventures, and when they're together, they are unstoppable.

Belle

Life in a castle can be fun – but not if you live with a grumpy Beast! Belle has volunteered to keep him company. At least she also has the friendly enchanted household objects to talk to.

HAVE I GOT A STORY FOR YOU!

Beast

The Beast is scary but he can be kind, too. He is really a prince under a spell. It can only be broken if he falls in love with someone who loves him, too.

4

Aurora

When a bad fairy put a curse on Princess Aurora, good fairy Merryweather used her magic to alter it. According to the curse, when she turns 16, Aurora will prick her finger on a spindle and go to sleep.

Merryweather

Merrywather, along with fairies Flora and Fauna raise Aurora in their cottage in the woods. By not telling her that she is actually a princess, they hope to keep her safe from harm.

Ariel

Little mermaid Ariel is intrigued by humans. In underwater Atlantica, she can often be heard singing about the human world. Is it really as dangerous as King Triton says? Headstrong Ariel wants to know!

Ursula

Sea witch Ursula wants to rule Atlantica. She hopes to gain power over King Triton by getting his daughter into danger in the human world.

MEET CINDERELLA

Cinderella spends every day sweeping, scrubbing and dusting for her stepmother and stepsisters. They're so mean! They never let her go out and have fun. She has to dress in rags, too. However, today there is a fair in the village – and Cinderella has an invite! She has put on a gorgeous blue dress made by her Fairy Godmother.

Fairy Godmother

Cinderella's Fairy Godmother wears a purple dress and a cloak tied with a pretty bow. With a wave of her magic wand, she makes Cinderella's wishes come true.

Elegant blue headband

Invitation to the fair

Beautiful detailing

CINDERELLA'S CARRIAGE

In this magical carriage, Cinderella is sure to arrive at the fair in style. It's a gift from her wonderful Fairy Godmother. With a wave of her wand and a pop of magic, Fairy Godmother made the carriage appear out of nowhere. What a beauty! Look at the purple seating and fancy lanterns. And how about those shiny golden wheels?

TO THE FAIR!

Lanterns leave a trail of twinkling light

Gold thorn pieces give the carriage its elegant shape

The seat is just the right size for Cinderella

Large golden wheels

Cinderella uses a stepstool to reach the carriage

BUILDING INSTRUCTIONS

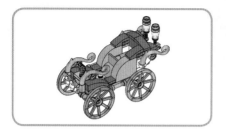

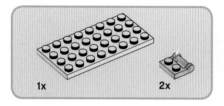

1x   2x

1

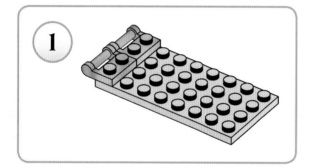

2

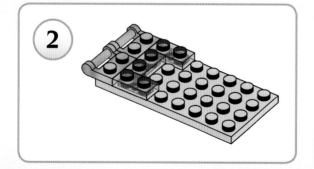

3x

2x   2x

3

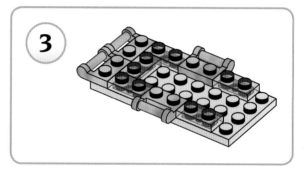

4x

4

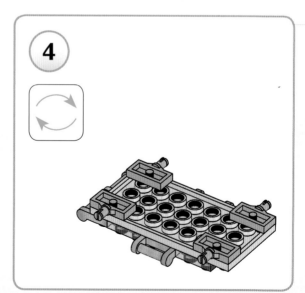

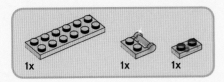

1x   1x   1x

5

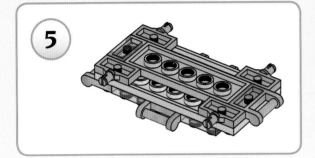

4x

6

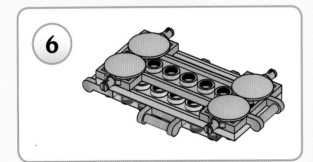

ONE STEP AT A TIME!

2x

7

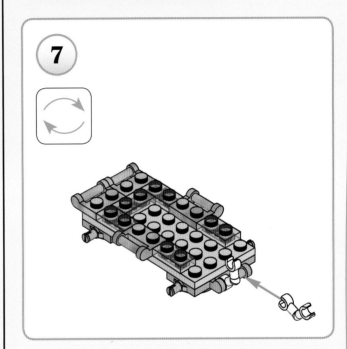

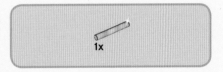

1x

8

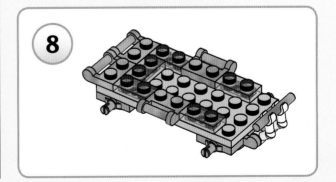

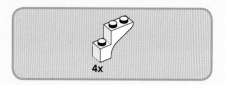

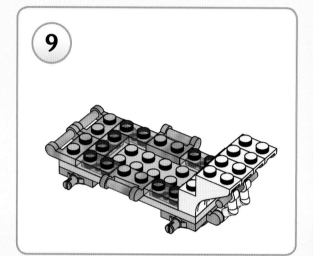

9

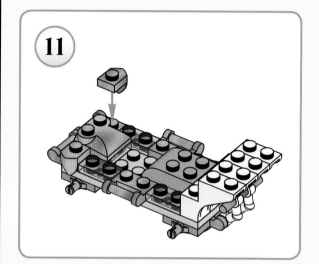

11

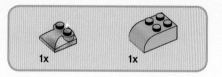

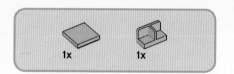

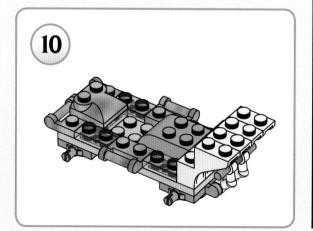

10

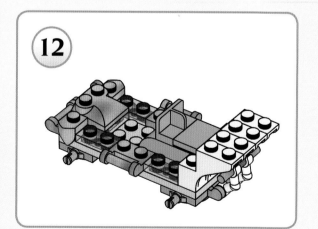

12

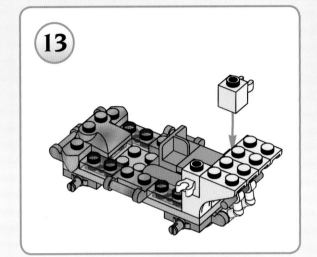

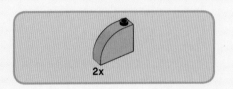

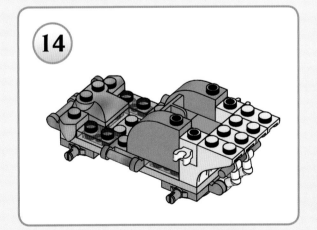

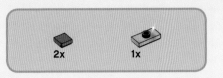

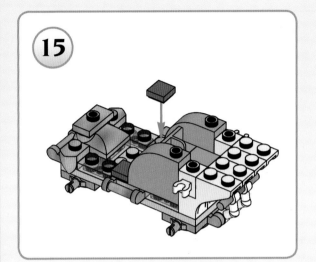

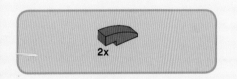

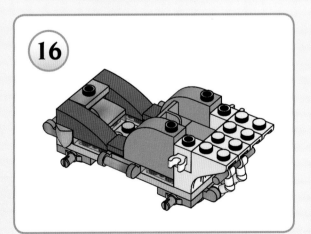

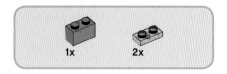

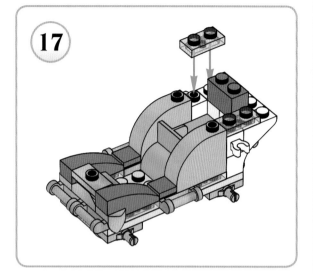

17

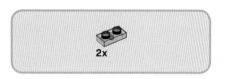

18

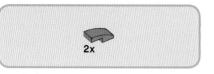

19

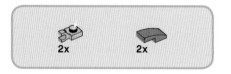

20

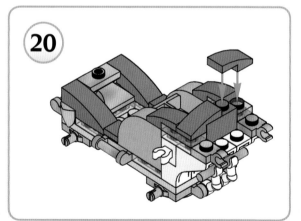

ALMOST DONE!

2x

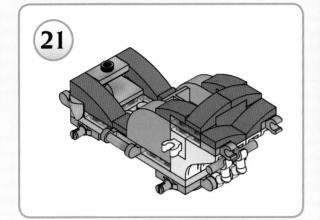

21

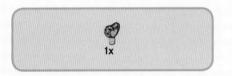

1x

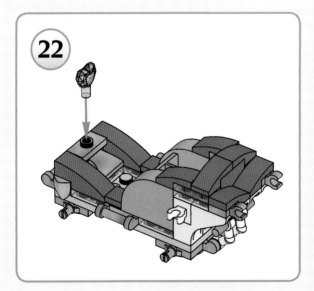

22

2x   2x

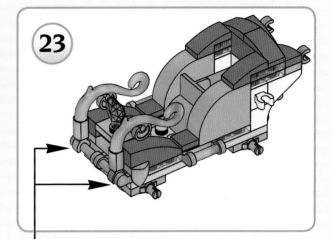

23

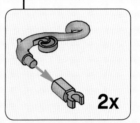

2x

2x

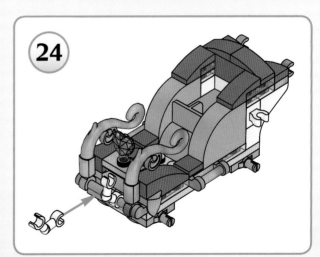

24

1x

2x 2x 2x

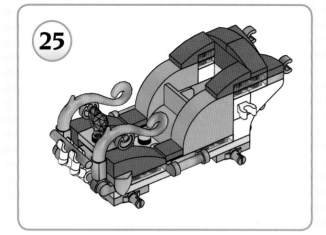

25

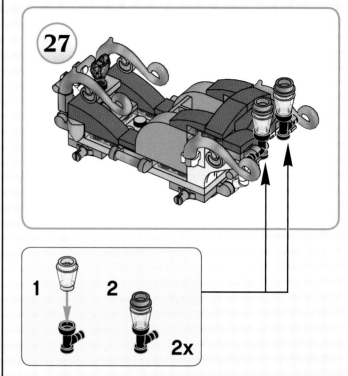

27

1 2

2x

2x

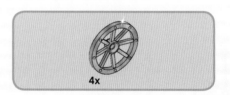

4x

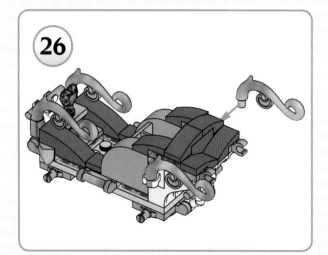

26

28

THIS WAY FOR ADVENTURE!

BUILD YOUR OWN ADVENTURE

In the pages of this book, you will discover an exciting LEGO® Disney Princess adventure story. You will also see some clever ideas for LEGO Disney Princess models that might inspire you to create your own. Building LEGO models from your own imagination is creative and endlessly fun. There are no limits to what you can build. This is your adventure, so jump right in and start building!

HOW TO USE THIS BOOK

This book will not show you how to build the models, because you may not have the exact same bricks in your LEGO collection. It will show you some useful build tips and model breakdowns that will help you when it comes to building your own models. Here's how the pages work...

"What will you build?" flashes give you even more ideas for models you could make

Sometimes, different views of the same model are shown

Breakdowns of models feature useful build tips

Special features or elements on models are annotated

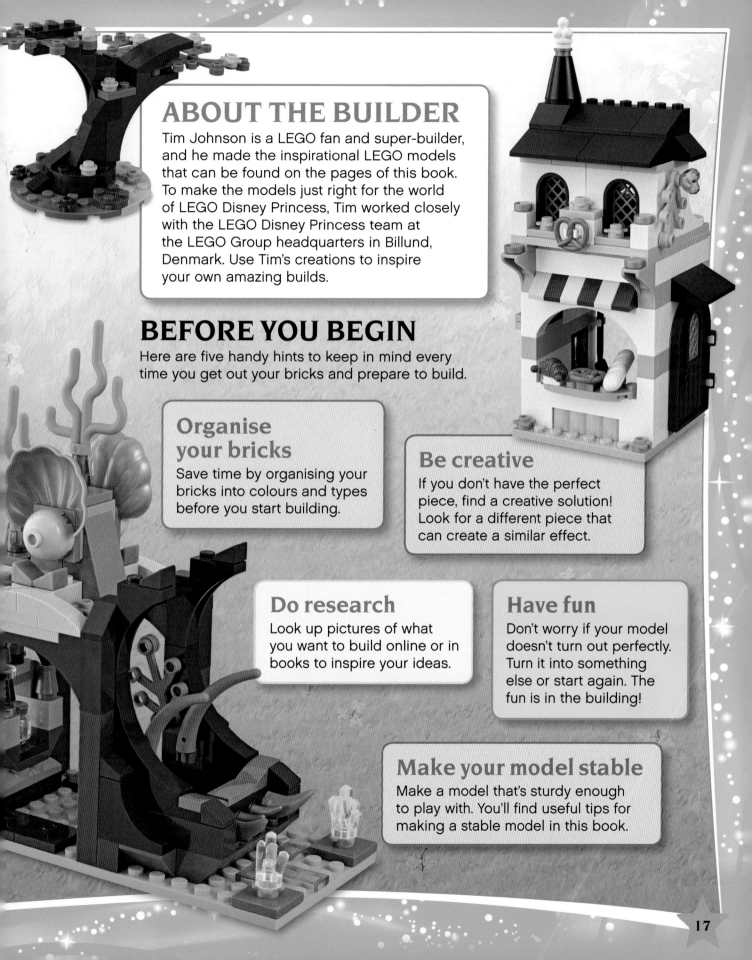

ABOUT THE BUILDER

Tim Johnson is a LEGO fan and super-builder, and he made the inspirational LEGO models that can be found on the pages of this book. To make the models just right for the world of LEGO Disney Princess, Tim worked closely with the LEGO Disney Princess team at the LEGO Group headquarters in Billund, Denmark. Use Tim's creations to inspire your own amazing builds.

BEFORE YOU BEGIN

Here are five handy hints to keep in mind every time you get out your bricks and prepare to build.

Organise your bricks

Save time by organising your bricks into colours and types before you start building.

Be creative

If you don't have the perfect piece, find a creative solution! Look for a different piece that can create a similar effect.

Do research

Look up pictures of what you want to build online or in books to inspire your ideas.

Have fun

Don't worry if your model doesn't turn out perfectly. Turn it into something else or start again. The fun is in the building!

Make your model stable

Make a model that's sturdy enough to play with. You'll find useful tips for making a stable model in this book.

BUILDER TALK

Did you know that LEGO® builders have their own language? You will find the terms below used a lot in this book. Here's what they all mean...

WHAT WILL YOU BUILD?

STUD

Round raised bumps on top of bricks and plates are called studs. A string has a single stud at each end. Studs fit into "tubes", which are on the bottom of bricks and plates.

2x2 corner plate

String with studs

MEASUREMENTS

Builders describe the size of LEGO pieces according to the number of studs on them. If a brick has 2 studs across and 3 up, it's a 2x3 brick. If a piece is tall, it has a third number that tells its height in standard bricks.

2x3 brick

1x1x5 brick

BRICK

Where would a builder be without the brick? It's the basis of most models and comes in a huge variety of shapes and sizes.

2x2 brick

2x2 round brick

1x1 round brick

1x2 curved brick

1x2 grooved brick

1x2 textured brick

1x2 log brick

2x2 domed brick

PLATE

Like bricks, plates have studs on top and tubes on the bottom. A plate is thinner than a brick – the height of three plates is equal to one standard brick.

 =

3 plates = 1 brick

2x2 plate

1x1 tooth plate

1x2 jumper plate

1x1 round plate

4x4 curved plate

4x4 round plate

TILE

When you want a smooth finish to your build, you need to use a tile. Printed tiles add extra detail to your model.

1x6 tile

2x2 tile

1x2 printed tile

1x1 round tile

18

HINGE

If you want to make a roof that opens or give a creature a tail that moves, you need a hinge.

1x2 hinge brick and 1x2 hinge plate

Hinged plates

1x2 hinge brick and 2x2 hinge plate

SLOPE

Slopes are bigger at the bottom than on top. Inverted slopes are similar, but upside down. They are smaller at the bottom and bigger on top.

1x2 inverted slope

2x1x3 slope

CLIP

Some pieces have clips on them, into which you can fit other elements.

1x1 plate with clip

1x1 plate with clip

HOLE

Bricks and plates with holes are very useful. They will hold bars or LEGO® Technic pins or connectors.

2x3 curved plate with hole

1x1 brick with hole

1x2 brick with cross hole

2x2 round plate

PLANT PIECES

There are many LEGO elements just for creating plants. Use plant pieces like these to build trees and add greenery to your models.

1x1 flower plate

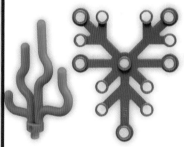

Seaweed

Large leaf element

Plant shoot

Bamboo leaves

Plant stem with flowers

Small leaf element

SIDEWAYS BUILDING

Sometimes you need to build in two directions. That's when you need bricks or plates like these, with studs on more than one side.

1x1 headlight brick

1x4 brick with side studs

1x1 brick with one side stud

1x1 brick with two side studs

1x2/1x4 angle plate

SPECIAL PIECES

Special pieces are used to create specific structures, or to link the build to a LEGO theme. These decorative pieces are all used in LEGO Disney Princess sets.

Heart-shaped jewel

Diamond jewel

Crystal piece

Crown piece

Transparent glitter dome

Gold thorn piece

Mini doll bow

Cupcake piece

1x1 glitter cone

Mini doll crown

Transparent magic wand

2x2 plate with petals

Flag

COME BACK, ARIEL!

CHAPTER 1
Ariel's speedy shell

KING TRITON'S PALACE

Deep under the sea, King Triton's daughter is singing. Ariel's song is all about the human world. Oh, if only she could visit it! Suddenly, a golden wheel floats down from above. Could it be from the human world? The little mermaid swims after it, her friends Flounder and Sebastian hot on her tail.

WELCOME TO ATLANTICA!

Ariel's stage

Ariel loves to sing, almost as much as she loves to explore. She practises her favourite tunes on a raised stage, complete with a microphone stand and a golden backdrop.

A grey angle plate allows pieces to be added in a sideways direction.

Gold shell piece

Grey 1x2/2x2 angle plate

WHAT WILL YOU BUILD?

- King Triton's throne
- Musical instruments
- Music stand

QUICK, FOLLOW THAT WHEEL!

LEGO® bar forms microphone stand

1x1 round plates decorate stage

6x6 round plate

Turntable base piece

2x2 tan brick

Platform building

The stage rotates on a turntable piece, which sits on top of a sturdy platform. The central section is made of two tan 2x2 bricks. These pieces are mainly hidden, so any colour can be used.

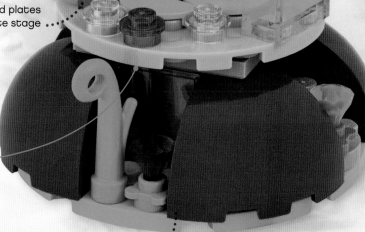

3x3x2 curved quarter dome

Matching model

These gates are symmetrical, so both sides look the same. Try and find pairs of matching pieces before you start building, if you want your builds to match, too.

2x2 curved brick

1x2 brick with side studs

Royal gates

King Triton is the ruler of Atlantica. The round gateway to his palace is made of curved arch pieces. Beautiful golden decorations, including a crown, make it truly fit for a king.

1x1x3 brick with clips holds gate

1x4x4 inverted half arch forms bottom of gateway

REAR VIEW

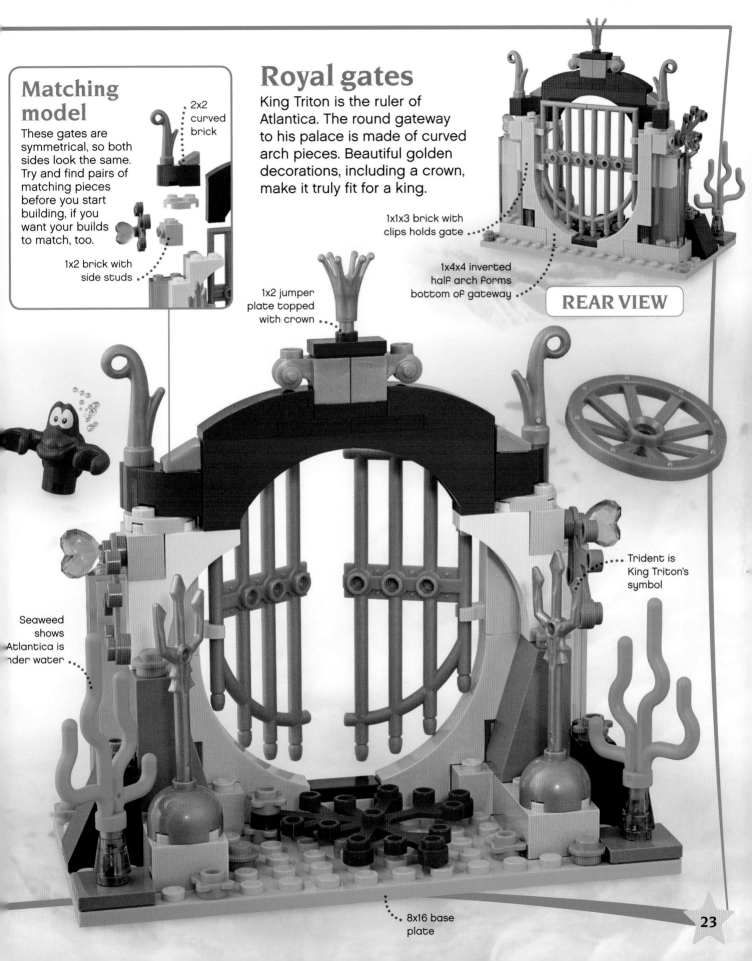

1x2 jumper plate topped with crown

Trident is King Triton's symbol

Seaweed shows Atlantica is under water

8x16 base plate

23

URSULA'S LAIR

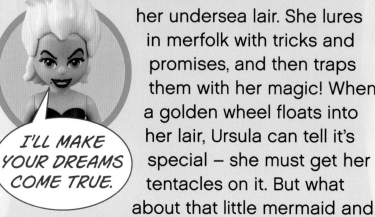

Ursula the sea witch lurks in her undersea lair. She lures in merfolk with tricks and promises, and then traps them with her magic! When a golden wheel floats into her lair, Ursula can tell it's special – she must get her tentacles on it. But what about that little mermaid and her fishy friends who are also after the wheel? They will just have to go!

I'LL MAKE YOUR DREAMS COME TRUE.

Ursula's lair

Sea plants and gems make Ursula's lair look friendly to passing merpeople. Watch out for the golden teeth and grasping tentacles that lurk inside!

Seaweed pieces camouflage this underwater lair

Curved pieces look like a mouth

Fang pieces slot into 1x4 brick with side studs

FRONT VIEW

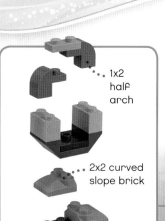

1x2 half arch

2x2 curved slope brick

Showpiece
A handful of small curved pieces make a home for tiny potion bottles. Exposed studs provide places to stick the bottles.

Bottles are a mix of tiny pieces

Potions cabinet
Sneaky Ursula has many magical potions that she uses to perform her tricks. Bright colours and transparent parts make the bottles look nice, but they might be hiding a nasty surprise!

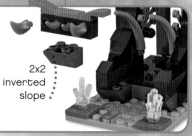

A row of inverted slopes creates a ledge that sits under a row of golden teeth.

2x2 inverted slope

SWIM INTO MY LAIR!

2x2 jumper plate

1x2/2x2 angle plate

A tall decoration on a simple stack of bricks adds height to your model. You can then cover the stack with other decorations, like these shells.

1x1 slope is tip of curve

2x2 domes look like giant, bulging eyes

WHAT WILL YOU BUILD?

- Witch's cauldron
- Gates to lair
- Watchtower

Potions stand fits neatly inside

Long, curved pieces look like fangs

Jumper plates let you move builds around easily

Transparent tiles add shimmer to the base plate

CORAL REEF

Ariel grabs the wheel and escapes, but Ursula chases her. As the little mermaid flees past a coral reef, she spots a giant shell and has a great idea. Ariel fixes the magic wheel to the shell, then jumps inside with Flounder and Sebastian. The shell whooshes off, taking them far away from the wicked witch. Bye, bye, Ursula!

WE NEED A GOOD PLAN!

WHAT WILL YOU BUILD?

- Sea creatures
- Underwater cave
- Shipwreck

Seaweed helps camouflage the vehicle in the reef

LET'S PROPEL THIS SHELL!

Spinning shell

Putting just a few elements together in an unusual way can create something completely new. A wheel, a shell and some seaweed combine to make Ariel a speedy getaway vehicle.

Golden wheel can spin freely

2x2 plate with pin

1x4 log brick

1x1 round tiles for smooth seat

Take a seat

The shell seat is locked firmly in place with a long log brick. The wheel attaches to a grey plate with pin on the back of the model.

Shell is the perfect size for Ariel's tail

A plate with clip holds a vine element and creates a natural-looking gap in the coral.

1x1 plate with clip

Coral reef

A coral reef is made up of all sorts of different shapes and colours – perfect for LEGO building! You can make your own version of this busy reef scene using whatever small pieces you have in your own collection.

A 2x2 plate with petals looks like a flowering sea plant

Vary thin and thick layers

Jumper plate makes it easy to add or remove pieces

A starfish sits on top of a sea anemone

Leaf element sandwiched between plates

Small stacks

Build small stacks using the same techniques as the stacks on the reef. Then you can easily move them around to expand your scene.

2x2 plate with petals

2x2 angled brick

Textured round brick looks like rough coral

27

THE BEACH

The wheel shoots out of the water, dropping the friends back into the sea and the shell onto the beach. Then the wheel vanishes! Ariel is thrilled to be so close to the shore. From behind a rock, she watches Prince Eric picnicking on the sand with his dog, Max. Eric picks up the shell to take home. Should Ariel find something to take home, too?

WHAT A BEAUTIFUL CASTLE!

Beach

Ariel wishes she could leave the sea and step onto the sand where Prince Eric sits. The divided beach scene is made of two large base plates: one tan and one blue.

WOOF!

I PACKED YOU A TREAT TOO, MAX!

Modular building

Why not try building a scene where you can easily swap the builds on top? This beach has been built with small sections of jumper plates and tiles, making it easy to move the builds around.

Remains of Ariel's spinning shell

Single stud connection makes it easier to remove items on top

Match builds to the spaces on your base plate

1x1 round gold tile

Place the rocks at any angle you wish

Sand-coloured plates hold sides together

Round plate for base

Make the picnic blanket by adding 2x2 tiles and jumper plates to a 6x6 base plate

MODULAR VIEW

28

Gold spike piece

Flag

Cone

Arch

Sandcastle

The castle is built using arches and slopes with cones and round bricks for turrets. It is decorated with jewels, a flower, and a flag held in place with a spike piece.

Don't forget a bucket and spade!

2x2x3 slope

4x4 round plate

Rocks

Make a cluster of rocks that is the perfect height for Ariel to hide behind. A handful of sloped bricks forms a natural rock shape.

1x2 slopes add detail to the tops of rocks

Transparent pieces look like crashing waves

SOUVENIRS

Back at the palace, Prince Eric sets Ariel's shell on his dresser. He wonders what other beautiful things there might be below the waves. He'd love to see! Inside her secret grotto, Ariel adds Eric's fork to the other human treasures she has collected. How it gleams! It must have been used at royal banquets galore. Oh, if only Ariel could go!

WHAT A FIND!

Eric's dresser

Eric's castle is decorated in rich, royal colours, such as golds and purples. His elegant dresser has scrollwork details and a smooth purple top. It is the perfect place to display the beautiful shell he found.

WHAT WILL YOU BUILD?

- Castle gates
- Castle fireplace
- Bed for Max

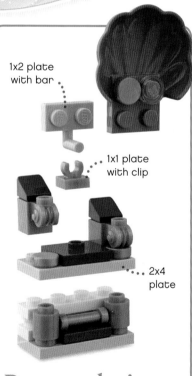

1x2 plate with bar

1x1 plate with clip

2x4 plate

Dresser design

This elaborate dresser is built simply around two stacked 2x4 plates. The shell attaches to a 1x2 plate with vertical bar, held in place by a 1x1 plate with clip.

Ariel's shell

Gold brick with scroll

Plate with horizontal bar hints at a drawer

Ariel's grotto

Ariel has been collecting trinkets for years and now her grotto is overflowing! This pile looks cluttered, but some clever construction makes it sturdy, too.

Make sure you add plenty of clip and stand pieces to hold Ariel's treasures.

1x1 tile with shaft

1x1 plate with clip

1x1 round plate with hole

4x4 round plate

Inverted slope

4x4 square turntable base

Offset layers

The pile is made up of three round plates. Inverted slopes placed between them create an uneven look, but give the plates plenty of support.

REAR VIEW

A golden crown tops the grotto

Colourful sea plants

CHAPTER 2
Aurora's adventure

AURORA'S DREAM

Shhhhh! Aurora is dreaming she is a princess, dancing in a castle ballroom. Her silk cape swirls as she twirls under a sparkling chandelier. When she hears someone coming, Aurora thinks it is her prince. But then – oh! She opens her eyes to find herself in bed at her cosy cottage. That is no prince – it's just Merryweather, coming to wake her up.

ONCE UPON A DREAM...

Aurora's bedroom

Aurora lives in a tiny cottage, hidden deep in the forest. It is practically built into the trees themselves! Adding plant elements to your buildings gives them a fairytale feel.

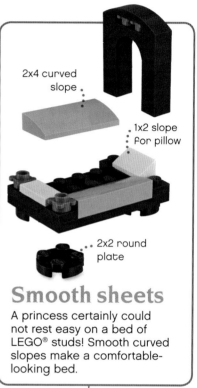

2x4 curved slope

1x2 slope for pillow

2x2 round plate

Smooth sheets

A princess certainly could not rest easy on a bed of LEGO® studs! Smooth curved slopes make a comfortable-looking bed.

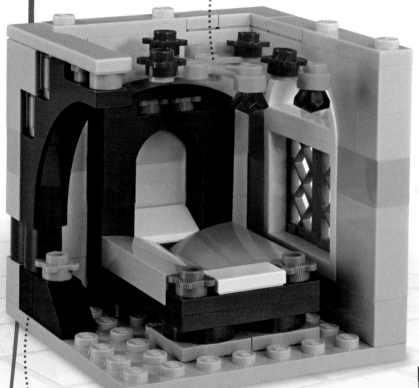

Leaf element decorated with jewels and flowers forms a canopy for bed

Tree is built right into the bedroom wall

Base is 6 studs long – a perfect fit for Aurora!

Pink flowers decorate headboard

WHAT A LOVELY DREAM!

Bar slots into brick with cross hole in ballroom ceiling

Chandelier

The ballroom's sparkling chandelier is built using upside-down pieces. This gives the look of crystals and lights dangling from the ceiling.

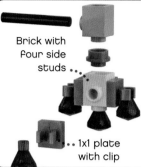

Bright idea

A central brick with four side studs holds all the chandelier pieces. It is attached by its base to a brick with a side stud that connects to a bar.

Brick with four side studs

1x1 plate with clip

Gem sits in top stud of brick

Brick with cross hole

Arches make an elegant ceiling

Turntable plate sits in the centre of the ballroom

Dream ballroom

The grand castle in Aurora's dream looks very different to her cottage. The ballroom has all-white pillars and a rotating turntable for her to twirl on.

Top technique

A pair of tall arches top the pillars in the ballroom, while a shorter pair cross to form a square. Tiles on top hide the studs for a polished look.

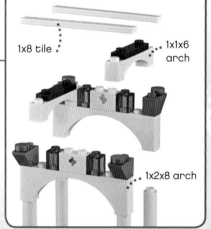

1x8 tile

1x1x6 arch

1x2x8 arch

Place the pillars and turntable on the base plate first, then fill in the gaps with smooth tiles

THE FOREST

Aurora loves to walk in the woods with her forest friends. One day, she settles down to rest in a pretty spot – a tree stump makes the perfect seat. She watches the animals gather at the pond, and spots a big spider's web on a tree. It looks so shiny and silky glistening in the sunlight. Aurora thinks it's beautiful.

WHAT WILL I SEE TODAY?

Hidden connection

A brick with clip is cleverly built into the trunk under the tree's leaves. It holds the spider's web securely and is hard to see on the finished model.

1x1 brick with clip

Half arch element

Leaf element holds pieces above and below

Mysterious blue fruit

Web in the woods

Aurora is surrounded by nature on her walk – spider's webs, fruit, flowers and bunny rabbits! This spider's web connects to a sturdy tree made of a variety of brown slopes, half arches and a canopy of leaves.

Large spider's web element

Connect smaller plates to make the base plate the size and shape you wish

Large slopes at base give the model stability

WHAT WILL YOU BUILD?

- Woodcutter's cottage
- Stack of logs
- Bird nest

Brown round plates and tiles make convincing tree stumps.

2x2 round plate

2x2 round tile

Shy fawn trusts friendly Aurora

WHAT DO YOU DREAM OF?

Tree stump seat

The forest is full of beautiful plants and wildlife. Aurora sits in the centre of it all on a cluster of tree stumps and small stones.

CHEEP!

Water lily floats on pond

Green slopes make mossy banks

Pond

Make a beautiful pond scene around a simple blue round plate by adding plant elements in and around it. Animals will soon flock to the water!

Small dish with toadstool printing

BRIDGE IN THE WOODS

Aurora decides to walk deeper into the woods, but her animal friends won't go with her. Why could that be? Aurora thinks they must be scared. The deep forest certainly does feel a little strange! Look, there is a spooky bridge with two glowing torches. And on the other side is a thick patch of thorns.

> TODAY IS A DAY FOR AN ADVENTURE.

> I WONDER WHO LIVES THERE?

Building bridges

Triangle plates in different colours divide the bridge into friendly and spooky sides.

White triangle plate

Grey triangle plate

Bright, light colours make this side look friendly

1x4x5 half arch

Bridge

Why not think of all the ways you can make a build look friendly or frightening, then use them all in one model! This bridge leads from Aurora's familiar woods to a scary scene on the other side.

WHAT WILL YOU BUILD?

- Stepping stones
- Bridge troll
- Spooky trees

Gold crystal
piece

Telescope
piece

2x2
jumper
plate

Dark light

Use the creepiest colours in your collection to build these spooky torches. A gold crystal placed at the top creates the look of a dimly glowing flame.

Wall of thorns

As Aurora crosses the bridge, the view isn't very welcoming! Dingy, angled plates make the ground on that side of the river look uninviting. A wall of prickly thorns blocks the path ahead.

Thorn
piece

Thorn in the side

These thorn pieces slot into the sides and top of a brick with four side studs. Change the angle of them to block a visitor's path!

Brick with
four side studs

Plant shoots
in different
colours hold
the railings

1x4 plates
used for
treads

Spooky,
pale rocks

A STRANGE DISCOVERY

Over the bridge looms a mysterious castle. Aurora is about to step inside when something golden catches her eye. She doesn't know it, but it's a magic spinning wheel. At Aurora's touch, the wheel starts to turn. Faster and faster it goes, until the jet of air picks her up and whisks her far away from the dangerous castle.

WHAT AN ODD SIGHT...

WHAT WILL YOU BUILD?

- Drawbridge
- Watchtower
- Dungeon

Gold thorn piece slots into 2x2 dome piece

Gold carriage wheel

Cone for spindle

WHAT A MAGICAL MACHINE...

Gold fez piece holds cone

Spinning wheel

A Sleeping Beauty story would not be complete without a spinning wheel. A golden carriage wheel is the perfect element to include in your own spinning build.

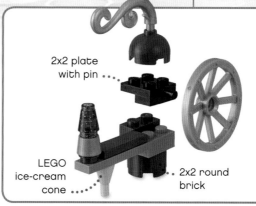

2x2 plate with pin

LEGO ice-cream cone

2x2 round brick

Perfect height

Work out how high you need to raise the plate with pin for the wheel to be able to spin before you begin. Here, an ice-cream cone piece and a round brick are just the right height.

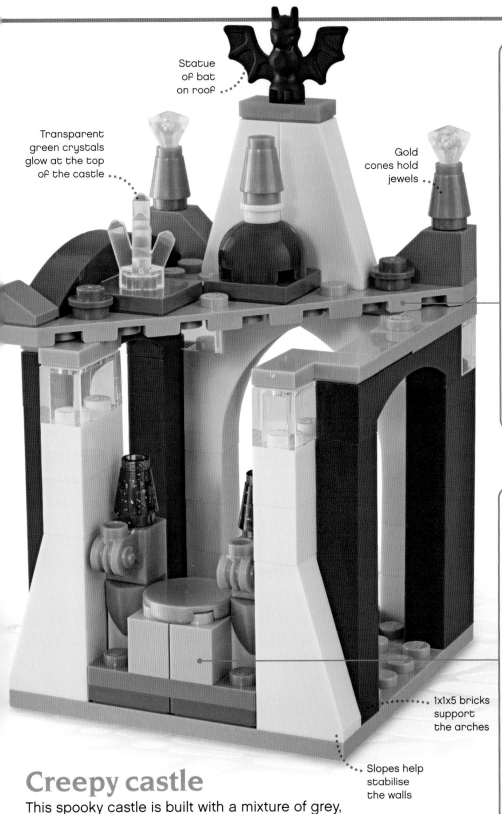

Statue
of bat
on roof

Transparent
green crystals
glow at the top
of the castle

Gold
cones hold
jewels

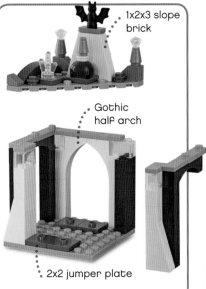

1x2x3 slope
brick

Gothic
half arch

2x2 jumper plate

Scary structure
Three large arches in spooky
shades make up three sides
of this castle. The half-roof is
an 8x8 triangular plate, with a
tower made from two slopes.

1x1x5 bricks
support
the arches

Slopes help
stabilise
the walls

Creepy castle
This spooky castle is built with a mixture of grey,
purple and pale-green bricks. These colours give
the castle a mysterious look, especially with the
striking green crystals glowing on the roof.

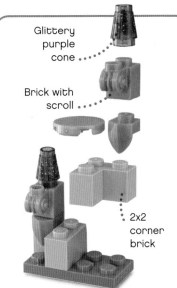

Glittery
purple
cone

Brick with
scroll

2x2
corner
brick

Throne room
Ornate handles make this
throne fit for a fairy – good
or bad! The base is made
from two 2x2 corner bricks.

AURORA'S COTTAGE

Merryweather is bustling around the kitchen. She is surprised to find Aurora back at the cottage so suddenly. She didn't see her whoosh in through the window! Aurora excitedly tells the fairy about her forest adventure. Merryweather smiles. "Oh, Aurora! You and your funny dreams!" she says.

> IT'S SO NICE TO BE HOME.

Cottage kitchen

With a tree growing through the middle, the cottage's kitchen is a charming mix between the outside and inside. It contains all the fairies need for cooking, cleaning and enchantments!

> LOOK OUT, YOUR CAKE!

1x2x8 arch piece

Merryweather's cake

Merryweather struggles to do household chores without using her magic. Her homemade cake is made to look lopsided using off-set layers and a hinge brick and plate at its base.

> BLUE ICING IS BEST.

Plate with petals looks like dripping icing

The second tier of the cake is attached to the jumper plate below by its edge. This makes it look like it is sliding off!

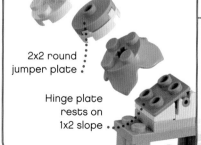

2x2 round jumper plate

Hinge plate rests on 1x2 slope

Simple table build is also used for the cabinet

Latticed window

Mix of textured and smooth bricks makes the cottage look old and weathered

REAR VIEW

Arch window piece

An arch window and a clear window piece create a fancy cabinet with an inset glass panel.

1x2x2 window element

Brown half arches and leaf elements create the tree

2x2 jumper plates let you move builds around easily

CHAPTER 3
Belle's invention

IT'S ABOUT TIME!

45

BELLE'S LIBRARY

The library is Belle's favourite place in the castle. She loves to get lost in a good book, sometimes for hours. Today, however, Belle can't concentrate on reading. It's a glorious sunny day – too hot to be inside! What a perfect day for a picnic in the garden with her friends. Belle checks that the Beast isn't around and then starts planning.

WHAT A BEAUTIFUL DAY!

WHAT WILL YOU BUILD?

- Belle's bedroom
- Writing desk
- Dining room

CAN YOU TURN DOWN THE HEAT, LUMIERE?

Beastly carving

Studs allow for another level to be built on top

Gold LEGO® book piece

Rounded pillars

Perfectly cut grass

Tan plates for flowerbeds

EXTERIOR VIEW

Making space

The outside of a half cylinder makes a fireplace inside the library, but leaves a gap outside. Make it a feature by filling it with a sculpture or other decoration.

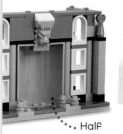

Two window pieces

Half cylinder

Elegant sculpture

46

Library

Belle's beloved library is bright and airy with white pillars and lots of tall windows. Unfortunately the fireplace makes it a warm place to be, too! Perhaps it is time to do some reading outside.

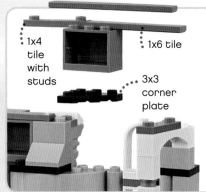

1x4 tile with studs

1x6 tile

3x3 corner plate

Library walls

A mix of plates and tiles lock in the large elements that are used to create the walls – a half cylinder, pillars, windows and arches.

1x6 arch

You could use plain plates or tiles as stacks of books

Build surfaces for Belle's friends to sit on

2x2 white plate

1x1 brick with scroll

Top tip

The decorative gold section of the fireplace rests on two scroll bricks. It is linked to the grey fireplace surround with a 2x2 white plate and purple jumper plate.

TIME FOR LUNCH!

VILLAGE MARKET

What does every picnic need? Tasty treats, of course! Belle heads off to the village market to buy goodies at the bakery. Along the way, she stops to admire the village fountain. She drops by the flower cart, too, and buys a sweet-smelling red rose. Belle is enjoying herself so much, she doesn't notice how quickly time is passing.

I HOPE THERE ARE CROISSANTS TODAY!

Fountain

This beautiful fountain sits in the centre of the village. It is filled with transparent blue pieces for water and gold tiles for coins. Belle has made many wishes in the fountain before!

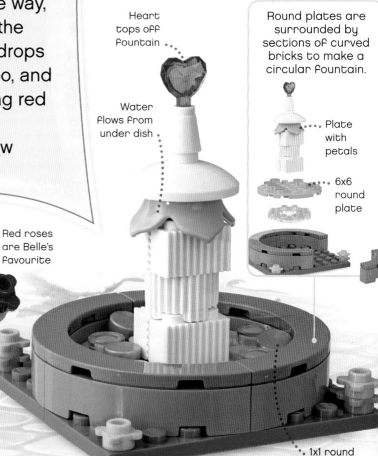

Heart tops off fountain

Water flows from under dish

Round plates are surrounded by sections of curved bricks to make a circular fountain.

Plate with petals

6x6 round plate

1x1 round gold tile

Red roses are Belle's favourite

Flower cart

Flowers aren't on Belle's shopping list, but she can't resist stopping at this small cart. The owner can wheel it around the village for selling door-to-door.

Flower sits in bigger leaf piece

Swap top

The key parts of a cart are the wheels and the handle. These attach directly to the cart base and are locked in place by wall pieces. The flowers are attached to two leaf elements, held together with a plant stem.

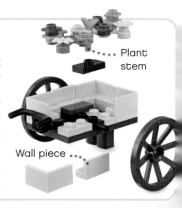

Plant stem

Wall piece

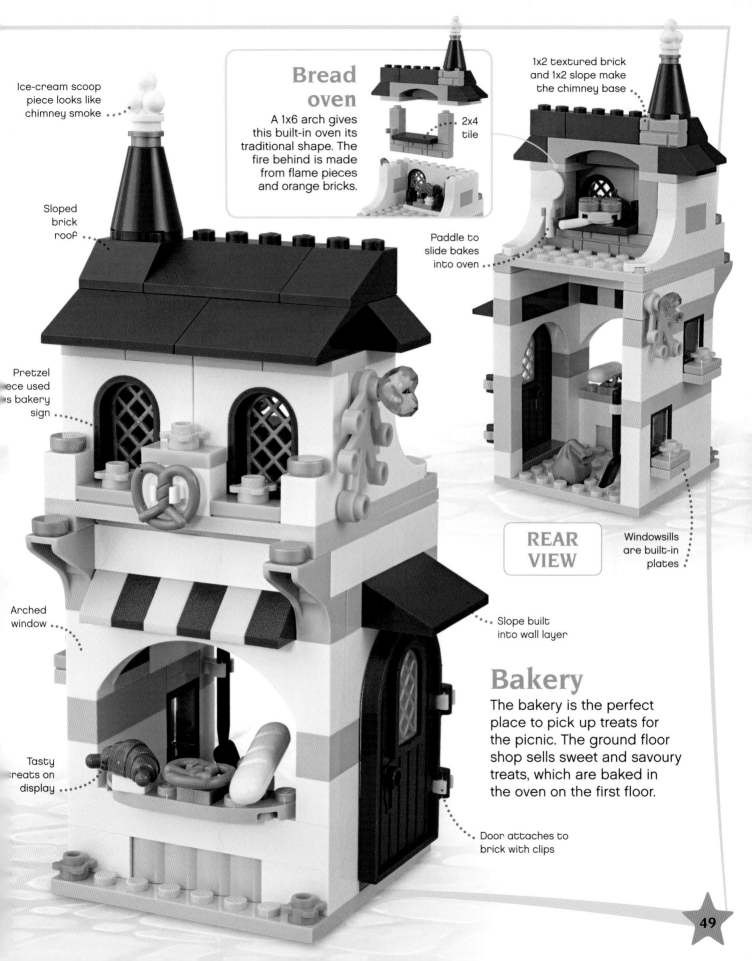

Ice-cream scoop piece looks like chimney smoke

Sloped brick roof

Pretzel piece used as bakery sign

Arched window

Tasty treats on display

Bread oven

A 1x6 arch gives this built-in oven its traditional shape. The fire behind is made from flame pieces and orange bricks.

2x4 tile

1x2 textured brick and 1x2 slope make the chimney base

Paddle to slide bakes into oven

REAR VIEW

Windowsills are built-in plates

Slope built into wall layer

Bakery

The bakery is the perfect place to pick up treats for the picnic. The ground floor shop sells sweet and savoury treats, which are baked in the oven on the first floor.

Door attaches to brick with clips

49

MAURICE'S WORKSHOP

Belle stops by her father's village workshop. Maurice isn't there, but his tools and inventions are. As Belle looks at them, a grandfather clock chimes. It reminds her that it is nearly time she was heading home. Belle hops onto her dad's vehicle. The wheels turn, and in a cloud of steam, the contraption takes off.

PAPA? WHERE ARE YOU?

Toolboxes

There are tools littering Maurice's workshop. Try building some toolboxes for storage. There are lots of ways to build handles for a traditional carry case, or just store items in a bucket!

LEGO bar

1x2 plate with vertical bar

Box build

Two double wall corner pieces create the shape of this tool box. They are attached to two 1x2 plates with vertical bars.

Mix and match colours for a makeshift look

Double wall corner

Clock maker

An angle plate holds the clock face of this detailed build. The pendulum is a LEGO® joystick attached to a LEGO Technic pin in a brick with a hole.

Angle plate

LEGO Technic pin

Brick with hole

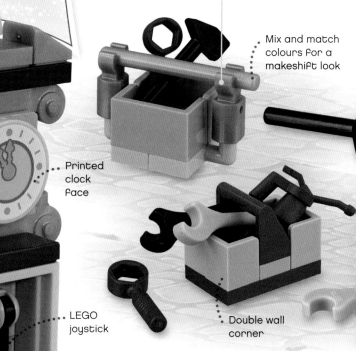

Printed clock face

LEGO joystick

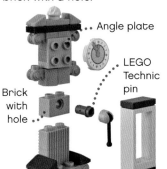

Messy Maurice has piles of tools!

Grandfather clock

Tick-tock! Maurice has been fixing this ornate gold clock. The printed clock face says it is almost midnight. Belle wonders if it belongs to a wealthy prince or princess from another kingdom.

Driver's seat

A large bracket piece creates a sturdy platform for Belle to steer from. It is locked in place with a 1x4 tile and a half cylinder piece.

1x4 tile

5x2x2 bracket

I HOPE THIS WORKS!

Maurice's machine

This curious contraption has been made from scrap materials, including three mismatched wheels. Use whatever bricks you have in your own collection and invent something new – just like Maurice!

Steam ahead

Make a cylindrical boiler out of two curved sections. It doesn't matter that they aren't the same height. Look for a creative solution, such as adding a furnace section on one side.

2x4x4 half cylinder

2x4x2 half cylinder

Transparent orange studs for fire

Icing-topped lamp makes an unusual topper!

Gold carriage wheel

Goblet is part of steam pipe

WHAT WILL YOU BUILD?

- Horse stables
- Furnace
- Workbench

CASTLE BALCONY

The Beast must not find out that Belle has been away! Belle hopes he is not watching as she zig-zags towards the castle on her dad's crazy contraption. It isn't the most sneaky of vehicles. As she jolts to a halt on the castle lawn, Belle is relieved to see the Beast fast asleep on the balcony. His snoring is just as noisy as the contraption!

WHAT A TRIP!

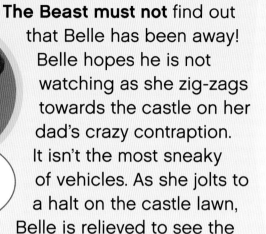

BANG!

Gold flag attaches to telescope

Enchanted rose is never far from the Beast's sight

Balcony

Try building different sections of a model, then combining them in a bigger build. This balcony is the same size as the library, so it fits perfectly on top. The Beast could see for miles – if only he were awake!

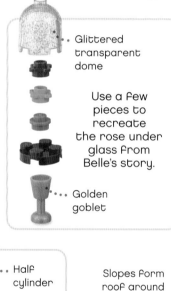

Glittered transparent dome

Use a few pieces to recreate the rose under glass from Belle's story.

Golden goblet

Slopes form roof around the balcony

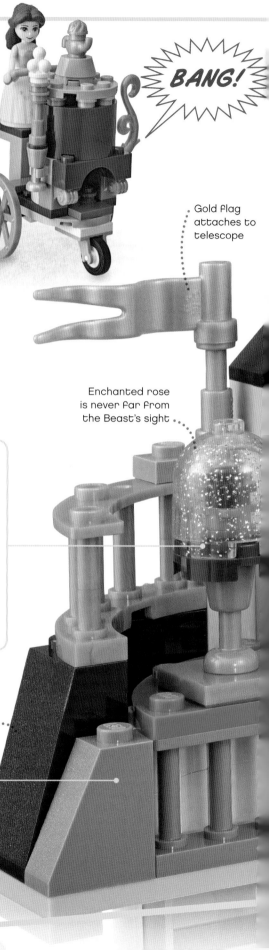

Outside walls

Railings are used to surround the balcony and underneath to support the floor. Green plates add to the look of a rooftop garden.

Half cylinder

White bricks support edge of plates above

Straight railings

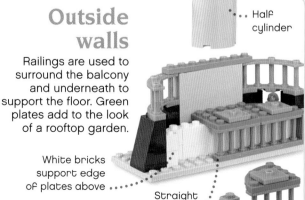

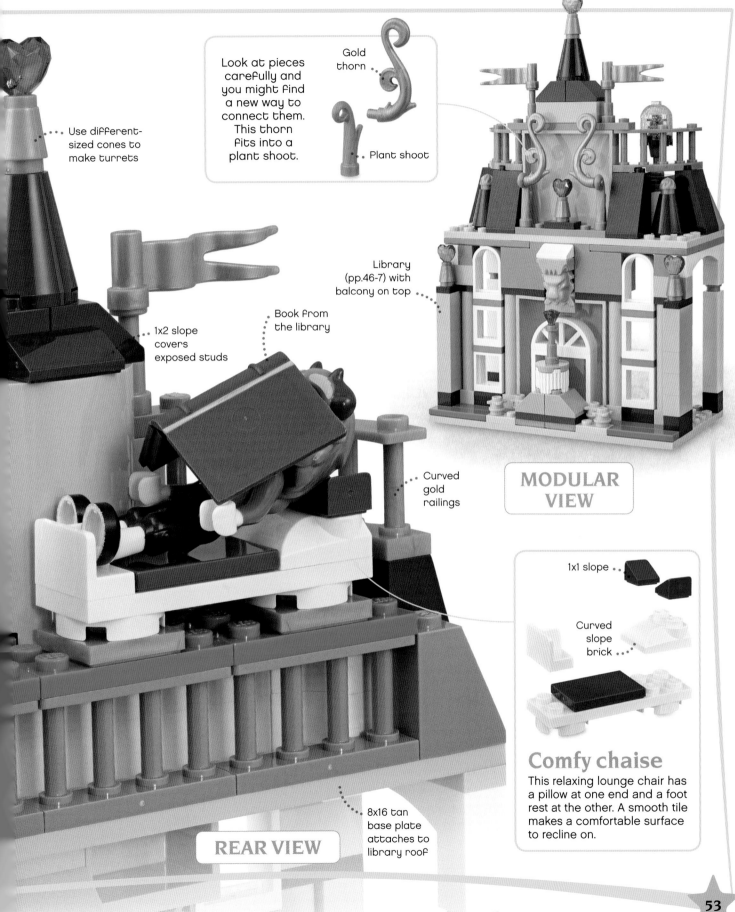

Use different-sized cones to make turrets

Look at pieces carefully and you might find a new way to connect them. This thorn fits into a plant shoot.

Gold thorn

Plant shoot

1x2 slope covers exposed studs

Book from the library

Library (pp.46-7) with balcony on top

Curved gold railings

MODULAR VIEW

1x1 slope

Curved slope brick

Comfy chaise

This relaxing lounge chair has a pillow at one end and a foot rest at the other. A smooth tile makes a comfortable surface to recline on.

8x16 tan base plate attaches to library roof

REAR VIEW

CASTLE GARDEN

It's picnic time! Belle's friends cheer as she enters through the garden archway. They help her unpack the cakes and put them out. There is fruit, chicken and a bottle of lemonade, too. It's all perfect! Then, just as the feast is starting, the Beast arrives. He has discovered the secret picnic! Luckily, he isn't angry. He just wants a bite to eat after his long nap.

WHAT A GREAT DAY!

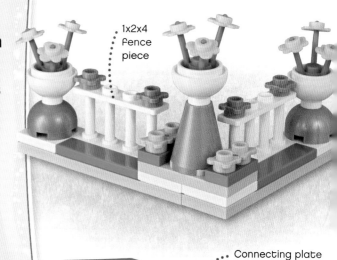

1x2x4 Fence piece

Connecting plate is decorated with flowers

Connected curve

Small plates with clips are used to attach the railings to the tops of two columns. The railings are held together with plates at the top of the arch.

Gold railing

1x2 plate

1x1 plate with clip

DON'T FORGET A SPOON!

1x1x8 column

Garden arch

Gold railing pieces are often used on the ground as fences. For this build, they have been rotated to make a beautiful plant-covered archway. What other pieces could you use in an unusual way?

Walls

The Beast's ornate garden is filled with carefully planted blooms, including pots along the walls. Build small sections that can be linked together in whatever shape you choose.

Making links

Individual sections of wall can be linked together by placing smaller ones on top. Just make sure to leave a space at one or both ends.

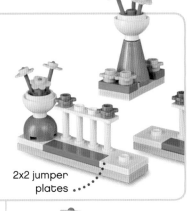

2x2 jumper plates

Brown 1x1 round plate looks like soil

Inverted dome

A small round plate holds the flowers firmly in place inside an inverted dome.

CUTLERY SLOWS ME DOWN...

Lemonade bottle

TIME FOR TEA!

Wobbly dessert

Picnic supplies

Display picnic food on a table covered with smooth tiles and jumper plates to attach food to. A regular bucket is transformed into a fancy ice bucket by adding a stand below and some cool transparent blue studs inside.

4x6 plate

Food connects to 1x4 plate with two studs

Table legs are 1x2x4 arches

WHAT A BEAUTIFUL SIGHT.

CHAPTER 4
Mulan's magic lantern

MULAN'S HOME

Mulan is in her room. She has been told to practise her calligraphy, but that's so dull. Practising martial arts moves would be much more fun! Never mind – it will soon be time for the lantern festival in the village. Mulan glances out of her window to see if it's dark yet. Above the magnolia tree in the garden, she sees a strange golden light.

I'M IN THE MOOD TO MOVE!

Magnolia tree

Mulan is named after the delicate magnolia tree that blossoms in her family's garden. The bench below is the perfect place for quiet thought, but Mulan doesn't like sitting still for long!

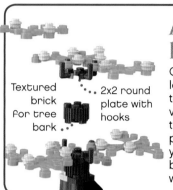

Textured brick for tree bark

2x2 round plate with hooks

Adding leaves

One way to attach leaves to a tree is to use pieces with vertical hooks. This trunk has round plates built in, but you could use bricks or plates with hooks instead.

Pale pink magnolia blossoms

Sloped tree trunk

Tea set

Martial arts practice

Mulan loves being active. She practises breaking planks of wood, just with her hands! Help her train by building two supports with smooth tiles on top so the planks don't get stuck!

1x2 log brick

1x4 tiles for planks

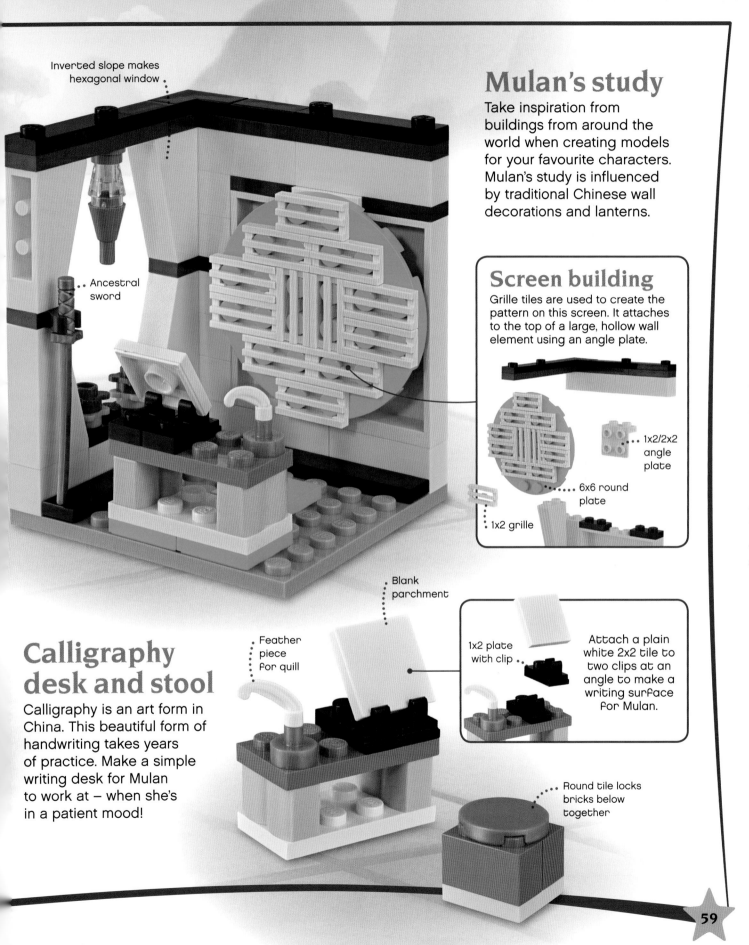

Inverted slope makes
hexagonal window

Ancestral
sword

Mulan's study

Take inspiration from
buildings from around the
world when creating models
for your favourite characters.
Mulan's study is influenced
by traditional Chinese wall
decorations and lanterns.

Screen building

Grille tiles are used to create the
pattern on this screen. It attaches
to the top of a large, hollow wall
element using an angle plate.

1x2/2x2
angle
plate

6x6 round
plate

1x2 grille

Blank
parchment

Feather
piece
for quill

Calligraphy
desk and stool

Calligraphy is an art form in
China. This beautiful form of
handwriting takes years
of practice. Make a simple
writing desk for Mulan
to work at – when she's
in a patient mood!

1x2 plate
with clip

Attach a plain
white 2x2 tile to
two clips at an
angle to make a
writing surface
for Mulan.

Round tile locks
bricks below
together

COUNTRYSIDE

The light is shining from a mountain top. What can it be? Mulan jumps on her horse, Khan, and rides off through the countryside, towards the light. Along the way, they stop at a well for a drink, and Mulan gathers some hay for Khan. Halfway up the mountain, she realises she is hungry, too. No problem! With her bare hands, Mulan catches a fish from a stream.

LET'S GO SEE WHAT IT IS!

Village well

Mulan stops to admire the beautiful well with its rich gold and magenta details. Five transparent round bricks on a blue background create the look of clear, sparkling water.

Create a decorative roof with four corner roof tiles on a round plate.

2x2 jumper plate

3x3 corner roof tile

1x6 round plate

1x4 arch brick

1x1 bricks make pillars

Well built

Each "petal" of the flower-shaped base is made from two 2x2 curved bricks and tiles. 1x1 bricks connect the four half-circles.

2x2 curved tile

Transparent round brick

1x1 brick

2x2 curved brick

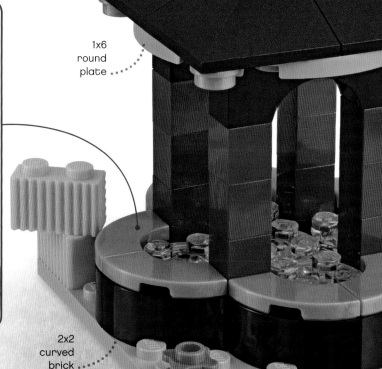

Snow-covered shrubbery

Slide fish down the curving stream

1x1 plate with tooth

1x2 plate with clip

Transparent blue elements and small white pieces look like ice and snow.

Molded rock wall element

Two slopes form a channel for the fish to slide into

WHAT A CATCH!

Snow easy

A LEGO® slide element can easily be disguised as a river by surrounding it in large grey rocky elements and a dusting of frosty snow pieces.

Blue slide element

Wall panel

Mountain stream

As Mulan climbs higher, the landscape is covered with snow. Ice-cold water flows through the streams. Ice-cold water and plenty of fish, that is!

UP HIGH

Brrr! It's snowy at the top of the mountain. Mulan lights a fire so she can get warm and cook her fish. While it's cooking, she builds a funny snow dragon to keep her and Khan company! She has already found out what the light is – a glowing lantern. It must have floated up from the lantern festival. Mulan decides to to go to the festival, and picks up the lantern.

THERE'S THE LIGHT, KHAN!

Lantern

Turn some square bricks into a circular build by mixing them with a few round pieces. This beautiful floating lantern is topped with a gold carriage wheel, showing that wheels aren't just for vehicles!

Half arch piece

Slope piece

White slope as snow pile

Inner secret

A bar connects the transparent yellow light and the wheel above. The rest of the lantern pieces are built on the round pink plate at the lantern's base.

Gold bar

Curved quarter tile

Transparent window piece

Snowy tree

This tree is built using a mixture of slopes and half arches. Heavy drifts of snow have gathered on top of the branches, leaving just the sturdy trunk showing.

Ice horns connect to a headlight brick

Transparent blue spikes

Round dragon egg

Claws fit onto plate with bar

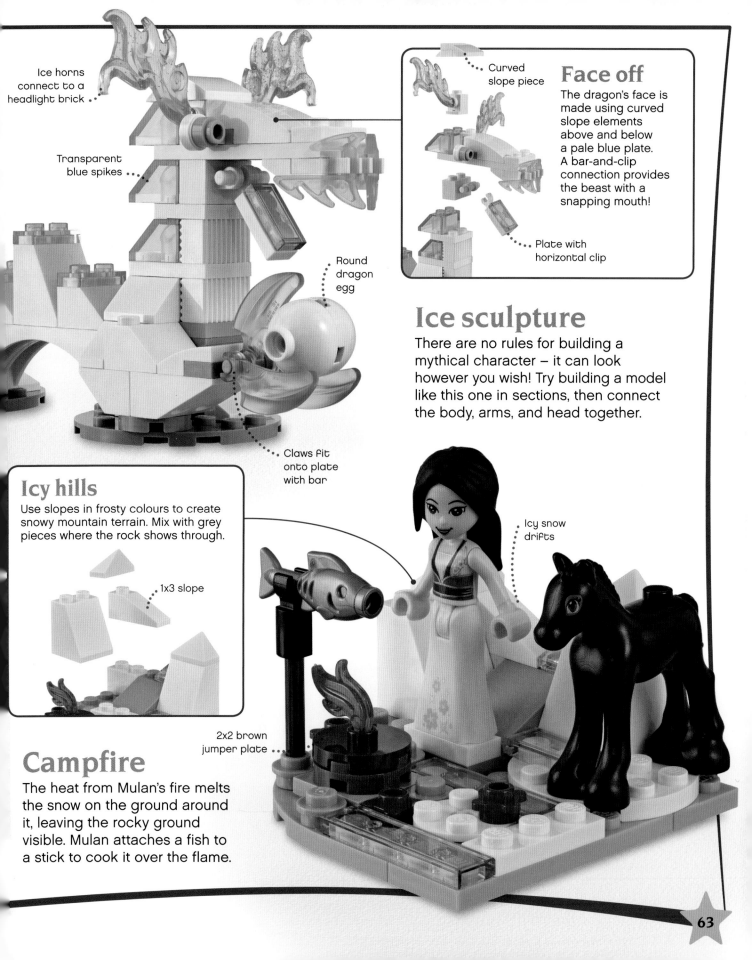

Face off

The dragon's face is made using curved slope elements above and below a pale blue plate. A bar-and-clip connection provides the beast with a snapping mouth!

Curved slope piece

Plate with horizontal clip

Ice sculpture

There are no rules for building a mythical character – it can look however you wish! Try building a model like this one in sections, then connect the body, arms, and head together.

Icy hills

Use slopes in frosty colours to create snowy mountain terrain. Mix with grey pieces where the rock shows through.

1x3 slope

Icy snow drifts

2x2 brown jumper plate

Campfire

The heat from Mulan's fire melts the snow on the ground around it, leaving the rocky ground visible. Mulan attaches a fish to a stick to cook it over the flame.

THE LANTERN FESTIVAL

The light from the lantern is so dazzling that Mulan shuts her eyes for a moment. When she opens them, she is back home – and the lantern festival is in full swing! Colourful lanterns flicker all around, lighting up the village gates and shining on Khan. There must have been magic on that mountain!

I CAN'T WAIT FOR OUR NEXT ADVENTURE!

Town gates

Ancient Chinese buildings often have distinctive features, such as columns and upturned roofs. Try to replicate these on your Mulan-themed models.

Clear building

A second layer of roof on these gates is supported using transparent pink bricks. These leave a visual gap but still support the pieces above.

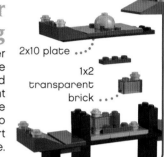

2x10 plate

1x2 transparent brick

Overhanging slopes at the end of each roof level

Exposed studs can be decorative, too

The two sides are mirror-images of each other

Wide and shiny polished wood columns

Ground can be any colour

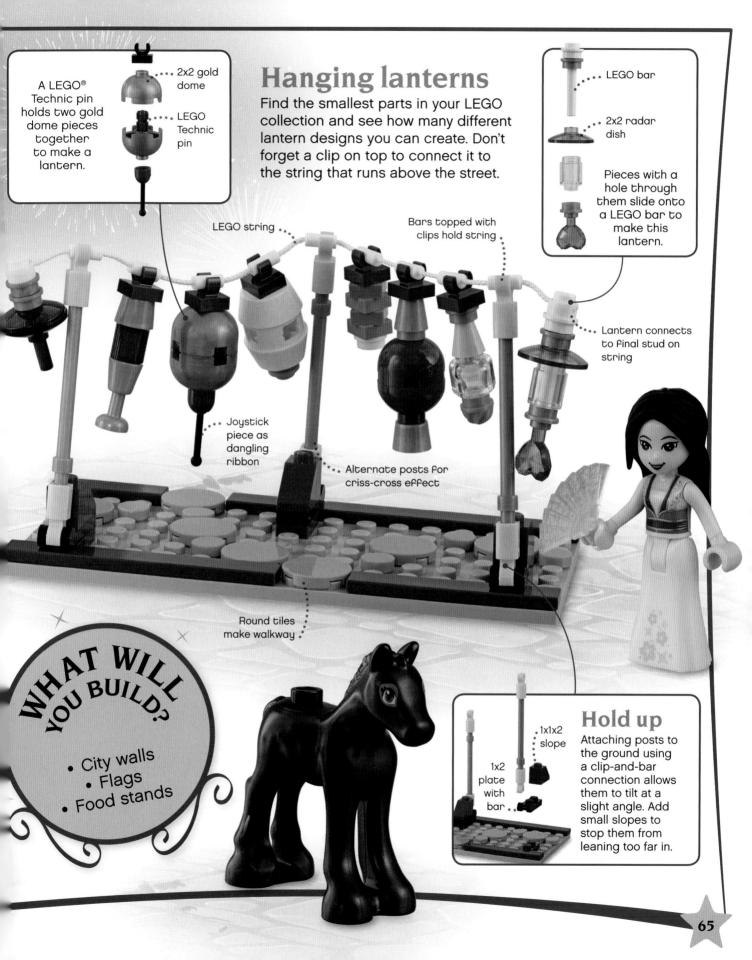

A LEGO® Technic pin holds two gold dome pieces together to make a lantern.

- 2x2 gold dome
- LEGO Technic pin

Hanging lanterns

Find the smallest parts in your LEGO collection and see how many different lantern designs you can create. Don't forget a clip on top to connect it to the string that runs above the street.

- LEGO bar
- 2x2 radar dish

Pieces with a hole through them slide onto a LEGO bar to make this lantern.

LEGO string

Bars topped with clips hold string

Lantern connects to final stud on string

Joystick piece as dangling ribbon

Alternate posts for criss-cross effect

Round tiles make walkway

WHAT WILL YOU BUILD?

- City walls
- Flags
- Food stands

Hold up

Attaching posts to the ground using a clip-and-bar connection allows them to tilt at a slight angle. Add small slopes to stop them from leaning too far in.

- 1x1x2 slope
- 1x2 plate with bar

65

CHAPTER 5
Cinderella's carriage

I HOPE
SHE BRINGS
BACK
SAUSAGES...

THE STABLES

Cinderella has been invited to the village fair, but there's a last-minute hitch. The wheels of her magical new carriage have vanished! Could a bad fairy have stolen them? Bruno the dog and Lucifer the cat think the wheels might have simply rolled away. They help Cinderella search for them. First stop – the stables.

WHAT AN EXCITING INVITATION!

Central turret

Use a 1x2 jumper plate to position your final bricks right in the middle of your model.

1x2 jumper plate

1x2 plate

Stables

The horses' stables look like a castle! Use a thin band of coloured plates to add detail to the model. 2x6 curved plates make overhanging lintels above the arches.

Curved plate for lintels

2x2x2 cone is a tiny turret

NEIGH!

Royal stables

White columns outside and gold pillars inside give the stables a regal look. Arches and plates lock them in place.

2x2 corner brick locks pillar in place

1x2x8 arch

1x3x12 arch

1x2x5 white brick

1x5 gold pillar

1x4 fence piece

1x2x8 arch

Clip holds horse's bridle

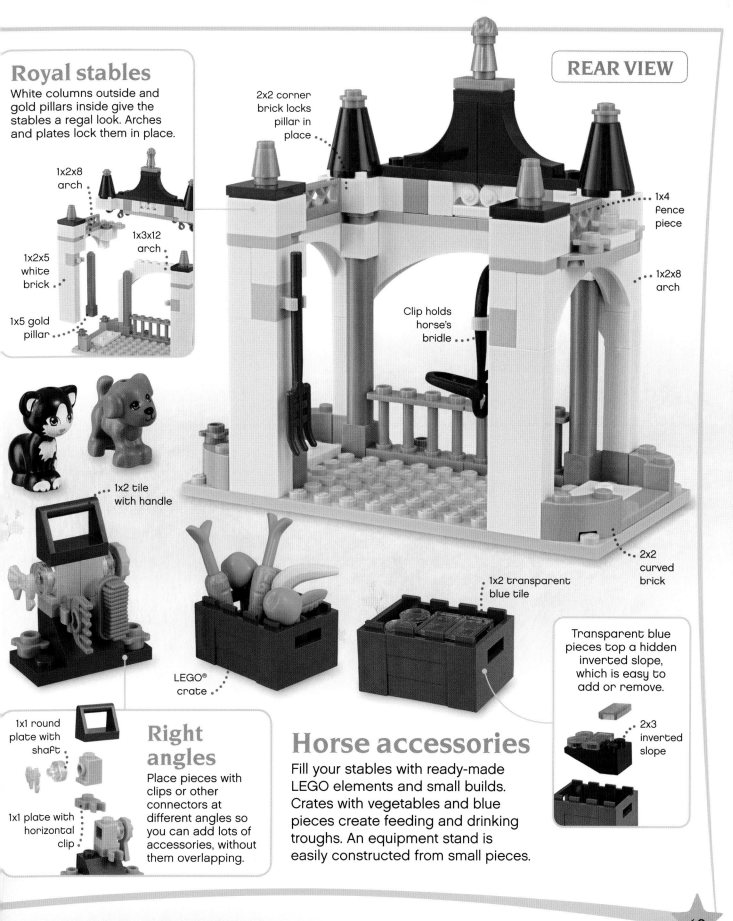

2x2 curved brick

1x2 tile with handle

1x2 transparent blue tile

LEGO® crate

Transparent blue pieces top a hidden inverted slope, which is easy to add or remove.

2x3 inverted slope

1x1 round plate with shaft

1x1 plate with horizontal clip

Right angles

Place pieces with clips or other connectors at different angles so you can add lots of accessories, without them overlapping.

Horse accessories

Fill your stables with ready-made LEGO elements and small builds. Crates with vegetables and blue pieces create feeding and drinking troughs. An equipment stand is easily constructed from small pieces.

AT THE HOUSE

The carriage wheels are still missing, but Cinderella isn't panicking yet. They might be in the house. She and Bruno search downstairs. They open cupboards, look under the kitchen sink, and even peek inside the oven. No, the wheels aren't there! Lucifer promises to check upstairs, but instead the lazy cat slips into his bedroom for a sneaky snooze!

WILL YOU HELP ME SEARCH?

WHAT WILL YOU BUILD?

- Stepsisters' rooms
- Wardrobes
- Pumpkin patch

Lucifer's bedroom

While Cinderella has to sleep in the kitchen, spoiled cat Lucifer has his own luxury bedroom. It has the same colour scheme as the kitchen but is completed with a comfy gold bed and lavish purple drapes.

Fit for a prince

Lucifer's bed is topped with gold cushions and tied with majestic purple bows. The bows attach to headlight bricks using round plates with shafts.

Headlight brick

1x1 round plate with shaft

Drapes are an arch build placed in front of wall, but not attached to it

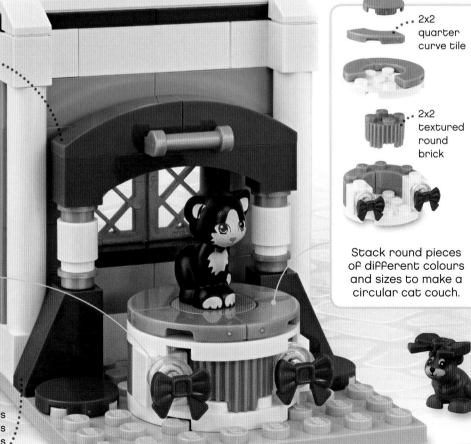

Slope pieces look like folds of drapes

2x2 quarter curve tile

2x2 textured round brick

Stack round pieces of different colours and sizes to make a circular cat couch.

Cinderella's kitchen

Cinderella spends a lot of time in the kitchen, cooking for her lazy stepsisters. The kitchen is built up from an 8x16 base plate with simple rectangular bricks. Bricks with clips and side studs built into the walls provide places to add accessories and decoration.

Ding dong

Bells in the kitchen are linked to Cinderella's stepsisters' rooms. They ring them when they want Cinderella's help. Faucet pieces attach the bells to grey headlight bricks built into the wall.

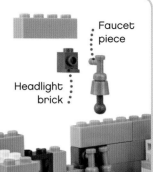

Faucet piece

Headlight brick

Door attached brick with clip

Roof beams are long white bricks

Add worktop build to finished room

SQUEAK!

Cinderella has been growing pumpkins in the kitchen garden

1x4 wall panel

1x2 log brick

Brick oven

Use brown and tan pieces to make an oven in the kitchen. Add a shelf on top to store equipment.

ROYAL GROUNDS

Cinderella's wheels aren't outside the house either. How baffling! She walks through the royal grounds when her Fairy Godmother appears. The fairy says she is sorry, but she used too much magic in making the carriage. That's why the wheels vanished. She can get them back, though. She waves her wand and does just that. One, two, three, four...

THANK YOU, FAIRY GODMOTHER!

Royal statues

The royal grounds are full of ancient statues, such as this tall urn. Why not build more pedestals like the one below, and add your own statues on top?

2x2 inverted dome ....

2x2 round jumper plate ....

Round plate with petals ....

On a pedestal

This elegant urn is displayed on a tall stone and marble pedestal made of 2x2 textured grey bricks and 2x2 textured round white bricks.

Fence posts are topped with crystal hearts ....

Smooth tiles make opening and closing the gates easy .

Park gate

Cinderella enters the royal grounds, where she finds Fairy Godmother. The grounds are bordered with an elaborate golden fence. The prince keeps the gates open for his subjects to explore the grounds.

Textured grey brick ....

Leaf layer

Leaf piece

To make sure your leaves stay firmly in place, sandwich them between a small plate and the half arch below. This will stop them from blowing away in the breeze!

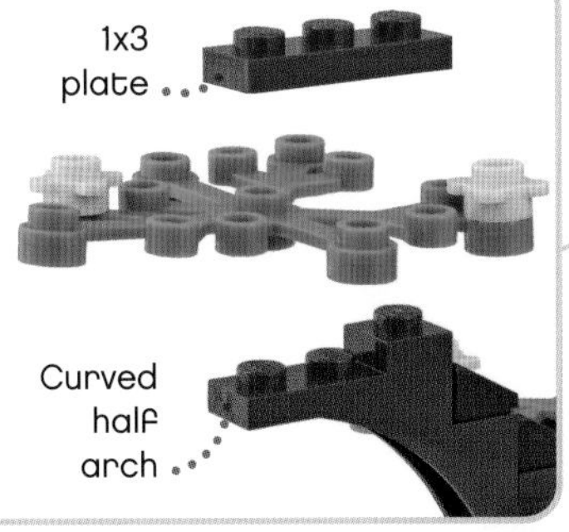

1x3 plate

Curved half arch

Flowering tree

Exotic plants, such as this yellow-flowering tree, grow in the royal grounds. Side-by-side semi-circular blue and green plates make a river bank for the tree to lean over.

Long half arch stretches over the water

I WILL GO TO THE FAIR!

BIBBIDI BOBBIDI BOO!

Use your carriage to go on more adventures!

WHAT WILL YOU BUILD?

- Exotic flowers
- Paved walkway
- Gazebo

VILLAGE FAIR

The carriage whisks

Cinderella to the fair and she's soon having fun! Cinderella tries bobbing for apples. It's harder than it looks! Fairy Godmother is having fun, too. She gets the top archery score without using magic! Later, Cinderella visits the refreshment stand where she meets a friendly young man. How charming he is.

WHAT A NICE WAY TO SPEND A DAY!

WHAT WILL YOU BUILD?

- Popcorn stand
- Coconut shy
- Bandstand

I'M HAVING SO MUCH FUN!

Spinning fruit

Make the game challenging by attaching the apples to a spinning turntable. Apple stalks make handy connectors.

Turntable element

Half barrel has studs in base

Steps raise Cinderella high enough to bob

Apples look like they are floating on water

Transparent ring plate

Bobbing for apples

Bobbing for apples is a fun fair activity, but it can get messy! Surround the base of a round barrel with transparent blue slopes and plates to look like overflowing water.

Display details

Top a simple base of bricks in alternating colours with curved plates for an overhanging display surface. A decorative roof draws the attention of passing customers.

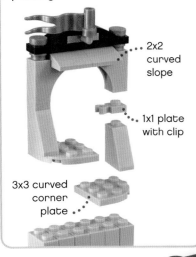

- 2x2 curved slope
- 1x1 plate with clip
- 3x3 curved corner plate

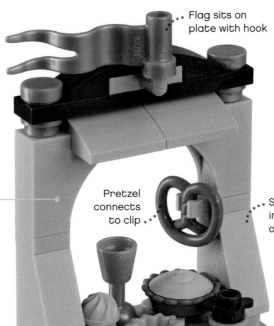

Flag sits on plate with hook

Pretzel connects to clip

Slope piece improves stability of arch

Refreshment stall

The man at the refreshment stall is Prince Charming! He takes a break from playing games and gets a pretzel. What a royal treat!

I SHOULD HOLD MY OWN PARTY.

Archery

An archery target needs different-coloured sections to score different points on. It doesn't matter which colours they are, but try to find bright ones. Fairy Godmother certainly will not miss it!

Centre is worth the most points

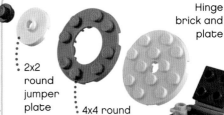

2x2 round jumper plate

4x4 round ring plate

Hinge brick and plate

Tilting target

Make a round target board with a 4x4 round plate, adding smaller circular pieces. Attaching it to a hinge brick and plate lets you set it up at an angle.

WHAT HAPPENED NEXT?

NOW I'VE BEEN TRICKED!

Ariel

After Ursula tricks Ariel to give up her voice, Ariel outsmarts Ursula. Ariel gets to keep her voice and stay in the human world.

Aurora

Aurora touches the spindle cursed by Maleficent and goes to sleep. But Maleficent can't stop Prince Philip falling in love with her.

GOOD NIGHT, MY DEAR.

Cinderella

In spite of her wicked stepsisters' attempts to stop her, Cinderella goes to the prince's ball. She has a wonderful time dancing – and meets Prince Charming.

Belle

Despite his gruff exterior, Belle can see that the Beast is good and kind. Belle's love breaks the spell on the whole castle.

THE SPELL IS BREAKING!

Mulan

Mulan becomes a brave warrior as she always dreamed she would. After her big adventure, she returns home to her father.

IT'S GOOD TO BE HOME!

Senior Editor Laura Palosuo
Project Art Editor Jenny Edwards
Pre-Production Producer Siu Yin Chan
Producer Louise Daly
Managing Editor Paula Regan
Managing Art Editor Jo Connor
Art Director Lisa Lanzarini
Publisher Julie Ferris
Publishing Director Simon Beecroft

Written by Julia March, Tim Johnson,
and Beth Davies
Inspirational models built by Tim Johnson
Photography by Gary Ombler

Dorling Kindersley would like to thank Randi Sørensen,
Heidi K. Jensen, Paul Hansford, Martin Leighton Lindhardt,
Camilla Jeppesen, Amy Corbett, Lam Quang Phan,
Carina Schou Lauridsen, and Charlotte Neidhardt at
the LEGO Group; Chelsea Alon, Samantha McFerrin,
Jean-Paul Orpinas, Scott Piehl, and Stephanie Everett
at Disney; Hannah Gulliver-Jones at DK for editorial
assistance; and Tori Kosara for proofreading.

First published in Great Britain in 2018 by
Dorling Kindersley Limited
80 Strand, London WC2R 0RL
A Penguin Random House Company

10 9 8 7 6 5 4 3 2 1
001–308282–Aug/18

A CIP catalogue record for this book
is available from the British Library.

ISBN: 978-0-24131-863-8

Printed and bound in China

A WORLD OF IDEAS:
SEE ALL THERE IS TO KNOW

www.dk.com
www.LEGO.com